Assessment

Columbus, OH

The McGraw-Hill Companies

SRAonline.com

 SRA

Send all inquiries to:
SRA/McGraw-Hill
8787 Orion Place
Columbus, OH 43240-4027

Printed in the United States of America.

ISBN 0-07-601861-X

2 3 4 5 6 7 8 9 MAZ 10 09 08 07 06 05 04

The *McGraw·Hill* Companies

Table of Contents

Unit 5 Balance, Emphasis, and Texture

Unit 6 Harmony, Variety, and Unity

Assessment in Art

"Assessment provides the basis for schools to be accountable to their communities for student learning in all subjects. As such, assessment is also an important part of a good art education. Assessment occurs during as well as after the art lesson. It provides some assurance that students are learning what teachers intend to teach."

—Carmen L. Armstrong

Designing Assessment in Art. National Art Education Association, 1994

Quality art programs require students to engage in problem solving, visual discrimination, and critical and creative thinking processes. These processes include visual memory, communication, comparing and contrasting, predicting, hypothesizing, and evaluating. Art education teaches key concepts and skills such as shape, color recognition, size differentiation, letter and number recognition, listening skills, sequencing, following directions, hand-eye and motor coordination, kinesthetic and spatial relationships, and direction and location. A valid assessment of an art program can demonstrate that students are, in fact, developing these essential skills.

There are a variety of ***Art Connections*** assessment tools available to art educators.

- **Blackline master assessments** in this book evaluate a student's understanding of the elements and principles of art presented in each lesson of the ***Art Connections*** program. There are 36 English and Spanish blackline master assessments, one for each lesson. These assessments can be used individually, following each lesson, or they can be grouped and used two or three times during a unit.

- **Evaluation Checklists** for Art History and Culture, Art Criticism, Aesthetic Perception, Creative Expression, and Portfolio Assessment presented on the following pages are intended to be flexible so that teachers can adjust them to various classroom and individual needs. These checklists can be used at the teacher's discretion. They are intended to be copied for each evaluation and may be kept in each student's art portfolio. Each accomplishment on the Evaluation Checklists is designed to be rated on a three-point scale.

    3—Established. The student's response or work demonstrates understanding and competence.
    2—Emerging. The student demonstrates some degree of knowledge and skill.
    1—Not yet. There is not yet evidence in the student's work that he or she has grasped the skill.

- **Creative Expression** rubrics provide valuable guidance for assessing the artwork that students create in class. There are 36 Creative Expression rubrics, one for each lesson in the ***Art Connections*** program.

Evaluation Checklists

Art History and Culture

Accomplishment	Not Applicable	Not Yet 1	Emerging 2	Established 3	Notes
Compares and contrasts artwork by different artists					
Recognizes artist's culture					
Recognizes artist's style					
Identifies artwork's place of origin					
Identifies artist's work					
Identifies subject matter of artwork					
Identifies cultural symbols in artwork					
Understands that art is practiced by all cultures, past and present					
Identifies time period of artwork					
Uses appropriate art vocabulary in describing, interpreting, or reflecting on artwork					

Art Criticism

Accomplishment	Not Applicable	Not Yet 1	Emerging 2	Established 3	Notes
Describes the elements and principles of art used in a work					
Analyzes artwork effectively					
Interprets the meaning and purpose of artwork					
Judges artwork according to specific criteria					
Uses appropriate art vocabulary in describing, interpreting, or reflecting on artwork					
Identifies a variety of art career opportunities					
Recognizes artist's purpose or main idea of the work					
Supports analysis, interpretation, and judgments with examples					

Evaluation Checklists

🔍 Aesthetic Perception

Accomplishment	Not Applicable	Not Yet 1	Emerging 2	Established 3	Notes
Describes the multisensory characteristics in a work of art					
Uses appropriate art vocabulary in describing, interpreting, or reflecting on artwork					
Recognizes connections between art and other disciplines					
Compares and contrasts visual characteristics of objects and subjects					
Recognizes similarities and differences between visual art and music, dance, and theatre					
Demonstrates ability to observe elements and principles of art in the environment					
Draws appropriate conclusions based on aesthetic perception					

🎨 Creative Expression

Accomplishment	Not Applicable	Not Yet 1	Emerging 2	Established 3	Notes
Knows the differences between materials, techniques, and processes					
Uses different media, techniques, and processes to communicate ideas, experiences, and stories					
Uses art materials and tools in a safe and responsible manner					
Understands and effectively uses the elements and principles of art to communicate ideas					
Creates original, imaginative, and inventive works of art in 2-D and 3-D					
Demonstrates skill and craftsmanship					

Name _____ Date _____ Lesson _____

Evaluation Checklists

Portfolio Assessment

Accomplishment	Not Applicable	Not Yet 1	Emerging 2	Established 3	Notes
Completeness: Artwork in portfolio meets assigned requirements					
Effort: Artwork demonstrates concerted effort					
Variety: Artwork in portfolio demonstrates a variety of media, techniques, and processes					
Skill: Artwork demonstrates ability to utilize elements and principles of art to communicate ideas					
Volume: Portfolio includes a sufficient amount of work					
Quality: Artwork demonstrates appropriate level of quality					
Risk-Taking: Artwork demonstrates taking risks in creating/choosing works that go beyond minimum expectations					
Growth: Artwork demonstrates improvement					
Self-Evaluation: Student shows awareness of strengths and weaknesses					

Line Direction

A. Drawing

Draw each kind of line in the corresponding box.

straight

curved

zigzag

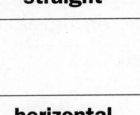

horizontal

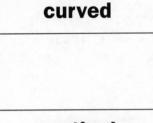

vertical

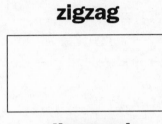

diagonal

B. Cutting

Cut out the squares that contain curved and diagonal lines. Paste them in the box below.

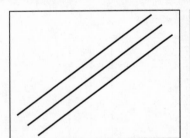

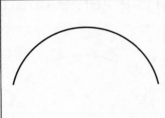

Dirección de la línea

A. Dibujar

Traza cada tipo de línea en el cuadro
correspondiente.

recta

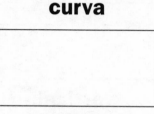

curva

en zigzag

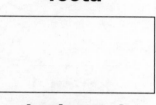

horizontal

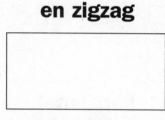

vertical

diagonal

B. Recortar

Recorta los cuadrados que contienen líneas curvas y
diagonales. Pégalos en el siguiente cuadro.

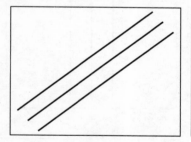 

Types of Lines

A. Matching

Draw a line to connect the name of a type of line to the picture that shows that line.

1. rough   **a.** ▬▬▬▬▬▬▬

2. smooth   **b.** ∿∿∿∿∿∿∿

3. broken   **c.** ——————

4. thick   **d.** - - - - - - - - - -

B. Drawing

Draw a picture using thin, thick, solid, and broken lines.

Tipos de líneas

A. Emparejar

Traza una línea para conectar el nombre de un tipo de línea y el dibujo que muestra esa línea.

1. áspera

a.

2. suave

b.

3. entrecortada

c.

4. gruesa

d.

B. Dibujar

Haz un dibujo usando líneas finas, gruesas, continuas y entrecortadas.

Name _____ Date _____

Calm Lines

A. Identifying

Circle the box or boxes that show calm lines.

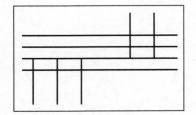  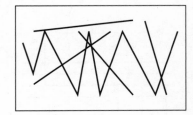

B. Drawing

Use a crayon to draw calm lines in the box below.

C. Fill in the Blank

Fill in the blanks in the sentence below with the correct answers.

The line directions of calm lines are _____ and _____ .

Líneas calmadas

A. Identificar

Haz un círculo alrededor del cuadro o de los cuadros
que muestren líneas calmadas.

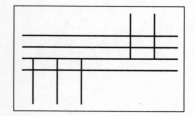  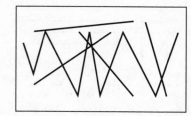

B. Dibujar

Usa un creyón para trazar líneas calmadas en el
siguiente cuadro.

C. Llenar los espacios en blanco

Llena los espacios en blanco de la siguiente oración
con las respuestas correctas.

Las direcciones de las líneas calmadas son
_____ y _____.

Active Lines

A. `Identifying`

Circle the box or boxes that show active lines.

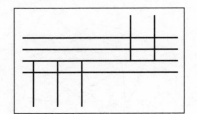 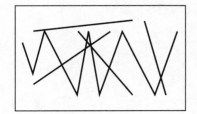 

B. `Drawing`

Use a crayon to draw active lines in the box below.

C. `Short Answer`

List three scenes you would draw using active lines.

Líneas activas

A. Identificar

Haz un círculo alrededor del cuadro o de los cuadros
que muestren líneas activas.

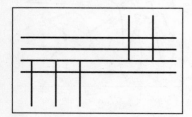 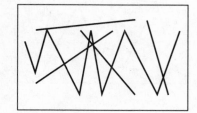 

B. Dibujar

Usa un creyón para trazar líneas activas en el
siguiente cuadro.

C. Respuesta corta

Alista tres escenas que dibujarías usando líneas
activas.

Geometric Shapes

A. **Drawing**

Draw three geometric shapes in the box below.

B. **Matching**

Draw a line to match each word with the correct shape.

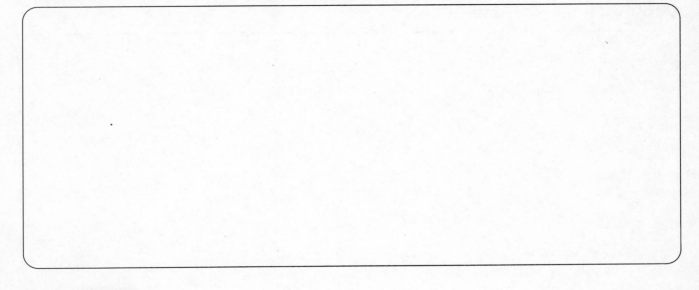

1. square   **a.**

2. triangle   **b.**

3. circle   **c.**

4. rectangle   **d.**

Figuras geométricas

A. Dibujar

Dibuja tres figuras geométricas en el siguiente cuadro.

B. Emparejar

Traza una línea para emparejar cada palabra con la figura correcta.

1. cuadrado   **a.**

2. triángulo   **b.**

3. círculo   **c.**

4. rectángulo   **d.**

Free-Form Shapes

A. `Identifying`

Circle the free-form shapes.

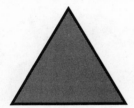   

B. `Drawing`

Draw three free-form shapes in the box below.

Figuras de forma libre

A. Identificar

Haz un círculo alrededor de las figuras de forma libre.

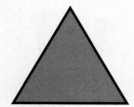   

B. Dibujar

Dibuja tres figuras de forma libre en el siguiente cuadro.

Name _____   Date _____

Geometric Forms

A. Matching

Match each geometric shape to its corresponding geometric form.

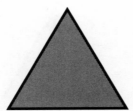

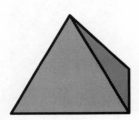
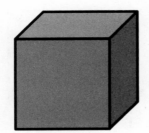

B. Matching

Draw a line to match the words that describe forms to the word *form*. Match the words that describe shapes to the word *shape*.

form   **shape**

flat   **three-dimensional**   **two-dimensional**   **depth**

Formas geométricas

A. Emparejar

Empareja cada figura geométrica con su correspondiente forma geométrica.

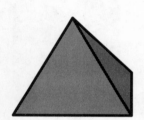

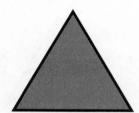

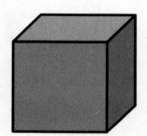

B. Emparejar

Traza una línea para emparejar las palabras que describen formas con la palabra *forma*. Empareja las palabras que describen figuras con la palabra *figura*.

forma   **figura**

plano   **tridimensional**   **bidimensional**   **profundidad**

Name _____ Date _____

Free-Form Forms

A. Matching

Match each picture to the correct word.

form   **shape**

B. Writing

Explain the difference between a free-form form and
a free-form shape.

_____

_____

_____

_____

_____

_____

_____

_____

_____

Formas abstractas

A. Emparejar

Empareja cada dibujo con la palabra correcta.

forma   **figura**

B. Escribir

Explica la diferencia entre una forma abstracta y una figura abstracta.

_____

_____

_____

_____

_____

_____

_____

_____

_____

Body Forms

A. Matching

Match each picture to the correct word.

form   **shape**

B. Drawing

In the box below, draw a picture of something on your body that is a form.

Formas corporales

A. Emparejar

Empareja cada dibujo con la palabra correcta.

forma   **figura**

B. Dibujar

En el siguiente cuadro, dibuja algo de tu cuerpo que sea una forma.

Name _____ Date _____

Animal Forms

A. Matching

Match each picture to the correct word.

shape

form

B. Short Answer

List three animal forms that you have seen.

_____

_____

_____

Formas animales

A. Emparejar

Empareja cada dibujo con la palabra correcta.

forma

figura

B. Respuesta corta

Alista tres formas animales que hayas visto.

_____

_____

_____

People and Space

A. Drawing

Draw three overlapping people in the box below.
Circle the one who is farthest away.

B. Writing

Explain what overlapping is.

Las personas y el espacio

A. Dibujar

Dibuja tres personas superpuestas en el siguiente cuadro. Haz un círculo alrededor de la que está más lejos.

B. Escribir

Explica lo que es superposición.

Name _____   Date _____

Objects and Space

A. Identifying

Circle the box or boxes that show overlapping.

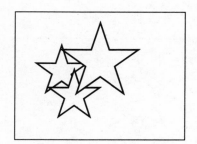   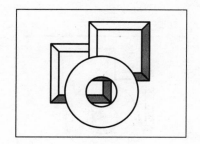   

B. Drawing

Draw three overlapping objects in the box below.

Los objetos y el espacio

A. Identificar

Haz un círculo alrededor de los cuadros que muestran superposición.

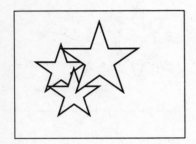 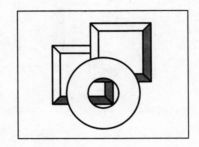 

B. Dibujar

Dibuja tres objetos superpuestos en el siguiente cuadro.

Color and Hue

A. Short Answer

Write the names of the primary hues.

a. _____

b. _____

c. _____

Write the names of the secondary hues.

a. _____

b. _____

c. _____

B. Coloring

Use crayons to color each box. Show which two primary hues are mixed to create each secondary hue.

☐ + ☐ = ☐ orange

☐ + ☐ = ☐ green

☐ + ☐ = ☐ violet

El color y el matiz

A. Respuesta corta

Escribe los nombres de los matices primarios.

a. _____

b. _____

c. _____

Escribe los nombres de los matices secundarios.

a. _____

b. _____

c. _____

B. Colorear

Usa creyones para colorear cada cuadro. Muestra cuáles dos matices primarios se mezclan para crear cada matiz secundario.

[ ] + [ ] = [ ] anaranjado

[ ] + [ ] = [ ] verde

[ ] + [ ] = [ ] violeta

Warm Hues

A. Coloring

Use crayons to fill in the circles with warm hues.

B. Drawing

Draw a picture using warm hues.

Matices cálidos

A. Colorear

Usa creyones para pintar los círculos con matices cálidos.

B. Dibujar

Haz un dibujo usando matices cálidos.

Cool Hues

A. **Short Answer**

Name three cool hues.

_____

_____

_____

B. **Drawing**

Draw a picture using only cool hues.

Matices fríos

A. Respuesta corta

Nombra tres matices fríos.

_____

_____

_____

B. Dibujar

Haz un dibujo usando sólo matices fríos.

Value

A. Ordering

Number the squares in order of value from light to dark, one being the lightest value and three being the darkest value.

_____   _____   _____

B. Coloring

Create seven different values from light (white) to dark (black).

C. Drawing

Draw a picture using three different values of gray.

Nombre _____ Fecha _____

El valor

A. Ordenar

Numera los cuadrados en orden de valor desde el más claro hasta el más oscuro, usando uno para el valor más claro y tres para el valor más oscuro.

_____   _____   _____

B. Colorear

Crea siete valores diferentes de claro (blanco) a oscuro (negro).

C. Dibujar

Haz un dibujo usando tres valores de gris diferentes.

Name _____   Date _____

Light Values

A. Short Answer

Explain what a tint is and how it is made.

_____

_____

_____

B. Coloring

Use crayons and fill in the circles with light values,
or tints, of blue.

 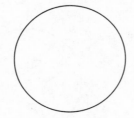 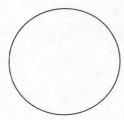

C. Drawing

Draw a picture using tints.

Nombre _____ Fecha _____

Valores claros

A. Respuesta corta

Explica lo que es un tinte y cómo se hace.

_____

_____

_____

B. Colorear

Usa creyones y llena los círculos con valores claros,
o tintes, de azul.

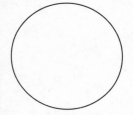 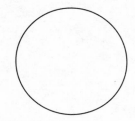 

C. Dibujar

Haz un dibujo usando tintes.

Dark Values

A. **Short Answer**

Explain what a shade is and how it is made.

_____

_____

_____

B. **Coloring**

Use crayons and fill in the circles with dark values,
or shades, of orange.

 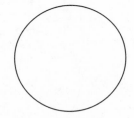 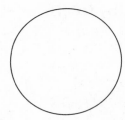

C. **Drawing**

Draw a picture using shades.

Valores oscuros

A. [Respuesta corta]

Explica lo que es un tono y cómo se hace.

_____

_____

_____

B. [Colorear]

Usa creyones y llena los círculos con valores
oscuros, o tonos, de anaranjado.

 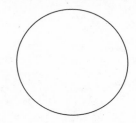 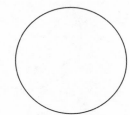

C. [Dibujar]

Haz un dibujo usando tonos.

Patterns

A. **Drawing**

Create a motif in the box below.

B. **Drawing**

Create a pattern using the motif you made in part A.

Los patrones

A. Dibujar

Haz un motivo en el siguiente cuadro.

B. Dibujar

Haz un patrón usando el motivo que hiciste en la parte A.

Patterns in Nature

A. Writing

Define *pattern* in your own words.

_____

_____

_____

B. Drawing

In the box below, draw an animal with a pattern on it.

Los patrones en la naturaleza

A. Escribir

Define *patrón* en tus propias palabras.

_____

_____

_____

B. Dibujar

En el siguiente cuadro, dibuja un animal que tenga
un patrón.

Rhythm

A. **Identifying**

Circle the words that are related to the word *rhythm.*

positive space

pattern

print

repeated

negative space

B. **Drawing**

In the box below, draw an object and repeat it to create rhythm.

El ritmo

A. Identificar

Haz un círculo alrededor de las palabras que se relacionen con la palabra *ritmo.*

espacio positivo

patrón

grabado

repetido

espacio negativo

B. Dibujar

En el siguiente cuadro, dibuja un objeto y repítelo para crear ritmo.

Rhythm and Form

A. Defining

Write the definition of the word *rhythm* in your own words.

_____

_____

_____

B. Writing

What is a storyteller doll? What is a diorama?

El ritmo y la forma

A. **Definir**

Escribe la definición de la palabra *ritmo* en tus propias palabras.

_____

_____

_____

B. **Escribir**

¿Qué es una muñeca cuentista? ¿Qué es un diorama?

_____

_____

_____

_____

_____

_____

_____

_____

_____

_____

_____

Diagonal Movement

A. Drawing

Draw a scene that shows diagonal movement in the box below. When you are finished, draw diagonal lines in your picture to show where your diagonal movement is.

B. Writing

Explain what diagonal movement is and how it is created.

El movimiento diagonal

A. Dibujar

En el siguiente cuadro, dibuja una escena que muestre movimiento diagonal. Cuando termines, traza líneas diagonales en tu dibujo para mostrar dónde está el movimiento diagonal.

B. Escribir

Explica lo que es el movimiento diagonal y cómo se crea.

_____

_____

_____

_____

_____

Curving Movement

A. Drawing

Draw a scene in the box below that shows curving
movement. When you are finished, draw curving lines
in your picture to show where the curving movement is.

B. Writing

Explain what curving movement is, why it is used,
and how it is created.

El movimiento curvo

A. Dibujar

En el siguiente cuadro, dibuja una escena que muestre movimiento curvo. Cuando termines, traza líneas curvas en tu dibujo para mostrar dónde está el movimiento curvo.

B. Escribir

Explica lo que es movimiento curvo, por qué se usa y cómo se crea.

_____

_____

_____

_____

Balance

A. Identifying

Circle the words that are related to the word *balance.*

symmetry

texture

axis

portrait

B. Drawing

Draw a balanced picture in the box below.

C. Short Answer

What is the difference between balance and symmetry?

_____

_____

_____

El equilibrio

A. Identificar

Haz un círculo alrededor de las palabras que se relacionan con la palabra *equilibrio.*

simetría

textura

eje

retrato

B. Dibujar

Haz un dibujo equilibrado en el siguiente cuadro.

C. Respuesta corta

¿Cuál es la diferencia entre equilibrio y simetría?

_____

_____

_____

Name _____ Date _____

Balance in People

A. **Writing**

Define *symmetry* in your own words.

_____

_____

_____

B. **Drawing**

Draw a person in a balanced pose in the box below.

El equilibrio en la gente

A. Escribir

Define *simetría* en tus propias palabras.

_____

_____

_____

B. Dibujar

En el siguiente cuadro, dibuja a una persona en una pose equilibrada.

Emphasis

A. `Defining`

Define the word *emphasis* in your own words.

_____

_____

_____

B. `Drawing`

In the box below, create a design. Emphasize one object in your design.

El énfasis

A. Definir

Define la palabra *énfasis* en tus propias palabras.

_____

_____

_____

B. Dibujar

En el siguiente cuadro, crea un diseño. Enfatiza un objeto en tu diseño.

Emphasis Using Contrast

A. Defining

How would you explain to someone what *contrast* is?

_____

_____

_____

B. Identifying

Read the choices below. Circle the choices that
describe how to create contrast.

place a large object next to a small object

place two objects that are the same hue next to each other

place a dark object next to a light object

C. Drawing

Create a drawing that has contrast in the box below.

El énfasis con el uso del contraste

A. Definir

¿Cómo le explicarías a alguien lo que es el *contraste*?

_____

_____

_____

B. Identificar

Lee las siguientes opciones. Haz un círculo alrededor de las opciones que describan cómo se puede crear contraste.

colocar un objeto grande al lado de uno pequeño

colocar dos objetos del mismo matiz uno al lado del otro

colocar un objeto oscuro al lado de uno claro

C. Dibujar

En el siguiente cuadro, haz un dibujo que tenga contraste.

Tactile Texture

A. Short Answer

What is *tactile texture*? How would you define *smooth*? How would you define *rough*?

_____

_____

_____

B. Short Answer

Write a word describing how each object feels on the blank next to the object's name.

feathers _____

desktop _____

brick _____

basketball _____

quilt _____

branch _____

glass _____

La textura táctil

A. `Respuesta corta`

¿Qué es la textura táctil? ¿Cómo definirías *suave*?
¿Cómo definirías *áspero*?

_____

_____

_____

B. `Respuesta corta`

En el espacio en blanco al lado del nombre del
objeto, escribe una palabra que describa cómo se
siente cada objeto.

plumas _____

superficie del escritorio _____

ladrillo _____

pelota de baloncesto _____

colcha _____

rama _____

vaso _____

Visual Texture

A. Short Answer

What is *visual texture*? How would you define *shiny*?
How would you define *matte*?

_____

_____

_____

B. Drawing

In the box below, draw a picture using visual texture.

La textura visual

A. **Respuesta corta**

¿Qué es textura visual? ¿Cómo definirías *brillante?*
¿Cómo definirías *mate?*

_____

_____

_____

B. **Dibujar**

En el siguiente cuadro, haz un dibujo usando textura
visual.

Harmony of Color

A. Identifying

Circle the descriptions of pictures that would have harmony of color.

a green house in a forest of green trees

a blue beetle on a red flower

a man dressed in orange looking at a sunset

a purple bat in a red room

B. Drawing

In the box below, draw a picture that has harmony of color.

C. Short Answer

What is *harmony*?

_____

_____

_____

La armonía de color

A. Identificar

Haz un círculo alrededor de las descripciones de los dibujos que tendrían armonía de color.

una casa verde en un bosque de árboles verdes

un escarabajo azul sobre una flor roja

un hombre vestido de anaranjado mirando una puesta del sol

un murciélago morado en un cuarto rojo

B. Dibujar

En el siguiente cuadro, haz un dibujo que tenga armonía de color.

C. Respuesta corta

¿Qué es armonía?

_____

_____

Harmony of Shape and Form

A. Writing

How do artists create harmony of shape and form?

_____

_____

_____

B. Drawing

In the box below, draw a picture that has harmony of shape.

La armonía de figura y forma

A. Escribir

¿Cómo crean los artistas la armonía de figura y forma?

_____

_____

_____

B. Dibujar

En el siguiente cuadro, haz un dibujo que tenga armonía de figura.

Variety of Color

A. Defining

Explain what *variety of color* is in your own words.

_____

_____

_____

B. Drawing

In the box below, create a picture that has variety of color.

La variedad de color

A. Definir

Explica lo que es *variedad de color* en tus propias palabras.

_____

_____

_____

B. Dibujar

En el siguiente cuadro, haz un dibujo que tenga variedad de color.

Variety of Shape and Form

A. Defining

How would you explain to someone what *variety* is?

_____

_____

_____

B. Identifying

Read the choices below. Circle the choices that
are examples of how to create variety of shape
and form.

place a square next to a circle in a design

make a sculpture using only pyramids

use many random shapes in a drawing

C. Drawing

In the box below, create a drawing that has variety of
shape.

La variedad de figura y forma

A. Definir

¿Cómo le explicarías a alguien lo que es *variedad*?

_____

_____

_____

B. Identificar

Lee las siguientes opciones. Haz un círculo
alrededor de las opciones que son ejemplos de
cómo crear variedad de figura y forma.

colocar un cuadrado al lado de un círculo en un diseño

hacer una escultura usando solo pirámides

usar muchas figuras al azar en un dibujo

C. Dibujar

En el siguiente cuadro, haz un dibujo que tenga
variedad de figura.

Unity in Sculpture

A. **Short Answer**

What is *unity*?

_____

_____

_____

B. **Drawing**

In the box below, create and sketch a plan for a sculpture that has unity.

La unidad en la escultura

A. Respuesta corta

¿Qué es unidad?

_____

_____

_____

B. Dibujar

En el siguiente cuadro, haz un plan y un boceto para una escultura que tenga unidad.

Unity in Architecture

A. Short Answer

What is *architecture*? What is an *architect*?

_____

_____

_____

B. Drawing

In the box below, draw a picture of a building that has unity.

La unidad en la arquitectura

A. Respuesta corta

¿Qué es arquitectura? ¿Qué es un arquitecto?

_____

_____

_____

B. Dibujar

En el siguiente cuadro, haz un dibujo de un edificio
que tenga unidad.

Answer Key

Unit 1

Lesson 1

A. Students will draw examples of curved, zigzag, horizontal, vertical, and diagonal lines in the appropriate boxes.

B. Students should cut and paste only the curved and diagonal line boxes.

Lesson 2

A.
1. b
2. c
3. d
4. a

B. Check students' pictures to make sure they have used the different types of lines in their drawing. You might want to ask students to point out the different types of lines they used.

Lesson 3

A. Students should circle the box containing only horizontal and vertical lines.

B. Students' drawings should contain horizontal and vertical lines.

C. horizontal, vertical

Lesson 4

A. Students should circle the boxes that contain curved, zigzag, and diagonal lines.

B. Students' drawings should contain diagonal, zigzag, and curved lines.

C. Answers will vary; however, the scenes that students are listing should contain some sort of action.

Lesson 5

A. Check students' boxes to make sure they have drawn geometric shapes. You might want to have them write the names of each shape below their drawing of that shape.

B.
1. d
2. b
3. c
4. a

Lesson 6

A. Students circle all shapes except the triangle and rectangle.

B. Check students' drawings to make sure they have drawn free-form shapes. Ask them to name their free-form shapes.

Answer Key

Unit 2

Lesson 1

A. Shapes and forms should be matched as follows: square/cube, circle/cylinder, and triangle/pyramid.

B. Students should match the words as follows: Form–three-dimensional, depth; Shape–two-dimensional, flat.

Lesson 2

A. The two free-form shapes should be matched to the word *shape,* and the two free-form forms should be matched to the word *form.*

B. A free-form form is three-dimensional. A free-from shape is two-dimensional. Both are undefined and organic.

Lesson 3

A. The two-dimensional boy should be matched to the word *shape.* The contoured, shadowed, three-dimensional boy should be matched to *form.*

B. Students should create a drawing of a body part. Encourage them to think about why this body part is a form.

Lesson 4

A. The two-dimensional pig should be matched to the word *shape.* The contoured, shadowed, three-dimensional pig should be matched to the word *form.*

B. To complete this list, encourage students to think of animals they have seen, such as pets or wild animals.

Lesson 5

A. Check to see that students have created overlapping people and have correctly circled the person who is farthest away.

B. Overlapping is when artists layer people or objects in a drawing. By covering up part of a person or object, the artist can create the illusion that the person or object is farther away from the viewer than other items in the work of art. This creates depth in a two-dimensional work of art.

Lesson 6

A. Students should circle the boxes containing stars and squares.

B. Check to make sure that students' drawings include overlapping. Ask students to point out the overlapping in their drawings.

Answer Key

Unit 3 **Lesson 1**

A.
  a. red
  b. blue
  c. yellow
  a. orange
  b. green
  c. violet

B. Students should color the boxes in the following way
  Line 1–red + yellow (or yellow + red) = orange
  Line 2–blue + yellow (or yellow + blue) = green
  Line 3–blue + red (or red + blue) = violet

Lesson 2

A. Students should color in the circles using shades of red, yellow, and orange.

B. Students' pictures should be made using reds, yellows, and oranges.

Lesson 3

A. blue, green, violet

B. Students' pictures should be made using only blues, greens, and violets.

Lesson 4

A. Students should number the squares in the following order: 3, 1, 2

B. Make sure students' coloring indicates a value progression from light to dark.

C. Check students' drawings to make sure they have used different values. Ask them to point out the different values to you.

Lesson 5

A. A tint is a light value of a hue or color. It is made by adding more white to the hue or color.

B. Make sure students have used tints of blue to fill in the circles.

C. Check students' drawings to make sure they have used tints. Ask them to point out different tints to you and identify what hue they are tints of.

Lesson 6

A. A shade is a dark value of a hue or color. It is made by adding more black to the hue or color.

Answer Key

B. Make sure students have used shades of orange to fill in the circles.

C. Check students' drawings to make sure they have used shades. Ask them to point out different shades to you and identify what hue they are shades of.

Unit 4 Lesson 1

A. Check students' motifs. Ask them how they created their motifs.

B. Check to see that students have repeated their motif to make a pattern. Did they change their motifs in any way? If so, ask them how.

Lesson 2

A. Pattern is a two-dimensional surface design composed of a motif.

B. Check students' pictures to make sure they drew a patterned animal. What motif did they use?

Lesson 3

A. Students should circle the following words: positive space, repeated, negative space.

B. Check students' drawings to make sure they have created rhythm. Ask them to point out the positive and negative space in their drawings.

Lesson 4

A. Rhythm is created by repeating an object throughout a work of art. Rhythm is composed of positive spaces separated by negative spaces. Rhythm creates movement in a work of art.

B. A storyteller doll is a Native American clay doll that illustrates an adult passing on the stories of the tribe to the younger generation. A diorama is a three-dimensional representation of a scene made with miniature figurines and objects.

Lesson 5

A. Check students' drawings to make sure they have created diagonal movement and drawn diagonal lines to highlight the diagonal movement.

Answer Key

B. Diagonal movement moves viewers' eyes through a work of art along diagonal lines and creates the feeling that the people or objects in the work of art are moving along diagonal lines. Diagonal movement is created by using rhythm and arranging the positive and negative spaces along diagonals.

Lesson 6
A. Check students' drawings to make sure they have created curving movement and drawn curved lines to highlight the curving movement.

B. Curving movement moves viewers' eyes through a work of art along curving lines and creates the feeling that the people or objects in the work of art are moving along curving lines. Curving movement is created by using rhythm and arranging the positive and negative spaces along curves.

Unit 5 Lesson 1
A. The following words should be circled: symmetry, axis.

B. Check students' drawings to make sure that they are balanced. Have students point out the axes in their drawings.

C. If something is balanced, it means that *similar* objects are placed on either side of the axis. If something is symmetrical, it means that the two halves of the axis are exact mirror images of each other.

Lesson 2
A. Symmetry occurs when two halves of an object are mirror images of each other.

B. Check students' drawings to make sure that they have positioned their people in balanced poses. Ask students if their people are also in symmetrical poses.

Lesson 3
A. Emphasis is when one object or area of a work of art stands out from the rest of the art.

B. Check students' designs to make sure that they have created emphasis. Ask students to point out the object they emphasized to you and explain how they created emphasis.

Lesson 4
A. Contrast happens when objects that are different are placed next to each other (for instance, a large object placed next to a small object).

Answer Key

B. Students should circle the following phrases: place a large object next to a small object, place a dark object next to a light object.

C. Check students' drawings to see if they created contrast. Ask them to explain how they created contrast.

Lesson 5

A. Tactile texture is texture you can feel. If an object is smooth, it feels even. If something is rough, it feels uneven.

B. Answers will vary. Examples include: feathers–silky; desktop–smooth; brick–rough; basketball–bumpy; quilt–fluffy; branch–scratchy; glass–smooth.

Lesson 6

A. Visual texture is texture you see, not feel. Shiny surfaces reflect light well. Matte surfaces do not.

B. Check students' drawings to make sure they create a drawing using visual texture. Ask them to describe the textures they used.

Unit 6 Lesson 1

A. Students should have circled the following phrases: a green house in a forest of green trees, a man dressed in orange looking at a sunset.

B. Check students' drawings to make sure they contain harmony of color.

C. Harmony is a principle of design that is created when objects in a work of art are similar.

Lesson 2

A. by repeating similar shapes and forms throughout a work of art

B. Check students' drawings to make sure they contain harmony of shape.

Lesson 3

A. Variety of color is what happens in a work of art when objects that are many different colors are placed together to create interest.

B. Check students' drawings to make sure they contain variety of color.

Answer Key

Lesson 4

A. Variety occurs when artists use different lines, shapes, and hues in a work of art to create interest and complicated relationships.

B. Students should circle the following phrases: place a square next to a circle in a design, use many random shapes in a drawing.

C. Check students' drawings to make sure they contain variety of shape.

Lesson 5

A. Unity is the feeling that parts of a work of art belong together. It is created by balancing harmony and variety.

B. Check students' sketches to make sure they illustrate unity. Ask the students to explain how their plans illustrate unity.

Lesson 6

A. Architecture is the study of buildings. People who design and plan buildings are called architects.

B. Check students' drawings to make sure they illustrate the concept of unity.

Creative Expression Rubrics

Level 2 • Unit 1 • Lesson 1

	Art History and Culture	Aesthetic Perception	Creative Expression	Art Criticism
3 POINTS	The student can compare two works of art featuring structures and identify the line directions.	The student accurately identifies line direction in the classroom.	The student's sculpture clearly illustrates a good use of line direction.	The student thoughtfully and honestly evaluates his or her own work using the four steps of art criticism.
2 POINTS	The student's identification or comparison is weak or incomplete.	The student shows emerging awareness of different types of line direction, but cannot consistently identify them.	The student's sculpture shows some awareness of line direction.	The student attempts to evaluate his or her own work but shows an incomplete understanding of evaluation criteria.
1 POINT	The student cannot compare two works of art featuring structures and identify the line directions.	The student cannot identify line direction.	The student's sculpture shows no understanding of line direction.	The student makes no attempt to evaluate his or her own artwork.

Level 2 • Unit 1 • Lesson 2

	Art History and Culture	Aesthetic Perception	Creative Expression	Art Criticism
3 POINTS	The student can identify how artists use different techniques to express types of lines.	The student accurately identifies types of lines in his or her environment.	The student's dream tree clearly illustrates a good use of types of lines.	The student thoughtfully and honestly evaluates his or her own work using the four steps of art criticism.
2 POINTS	The student's identification is weak or incomplete.	The student shows emerging awareness of types of lines but cannot consistently identify them.	The student's dream tree shows some awareness of types of lines.	The student attempts to evaluate his or her own work but shows an incomplete understanding of evaluation criteria.
1 POINT	The student cannot identify how artists use different techniques to express types of lines.	The student cannot identify types of lines.	The student's dream tree shows no understanding of types of lines.	The student makes no attempt to evaluate his or her own artwork.

Creative Expression Rubrics

Level 2 • Unit I • Lesson 3

	Art History and Culture	Aesthetic Perception	Creative Expression	Art Criticism
3 POINTS	The student can compare and interpret the styles of two works of art featuring water scenes.	The student accurately identifies calm lines in the classroom.	The student's water scene clearly illustrates a good use of calm lines.	The student thoughtfully and honestly evaluates his or her own work using the four steps of art criticism.
2 POINTS	The student's comparison or interpretation is weak or incomplete.	The student shows emerging awareness of calm lines but cannot consistently identify them.	The student's water scene shows some awareness of calm lines.	The student attempts to evaluate his or her own work but shows an incomplete understanding of evaluation criteria.
1 POINT	The student cannot compare and interpret styles of two works of art featuring water scenes.	The student cannot identify calm lines.	The student's water scene shows no understanding of calm lines.	The student makes no attempt to evaluate his or her own artwork.

Level 2 • Unit I • Lesson 4

	Art History and Culture	Aesthetic Perception	Creative Expression	Art Criticism
3 POINTS	The student can identify and make an interpretation of abstract art.	The student identifies that diagonal, zigzag, and curving lines create and describe excitement in a work of art.	The student's abstract painting clearly illustrates a good use of active lines.	The student thoughtfully and honestly evaluates his or her own work using the four steps of art criticism.
2 POINTS	The student's identification or interpretation is weak or incomplete.	The student shows an emerging awareness of active lines, but cannot consistently identify them or their purpose in a work of art.	The student's abstract painting shows some awareness of active lines.	The student attempts to evaluate his or her own work but shows an incomplete understanding of evaluation criteria.
1 POINT	The student cannot identify or interpret abstract art.	The students can not identify active lines or their purpose.	The student's abstract painting shows no understanding of active lines.	The student makes no attempt to evaluate his or her own artwork.

Creative Expression Rubrics

Level 2 • Unit I • Lesson 5

	Art History and Culture	Aesthetic Perception	Creative Expression	Art Criticism
3 POINTS	The student can identify and compare the use of geometric shapes in different works of art.	The student accurately identifies geometric shapes in his or her environment.	The student's paper collage clearly illustrates a good use of geometric shapes.	The student thoughtfully and honestly evaluates his or her own work using the four steps of art criticism.
2 POINTS	The student's identification or comparison is weak or incomplete.	The student shows emerging awareness of geometric shapes but cannot consistently identify them.	The student's paper collage shows some awareness of geometric shapes.	The student attempts to evaluate his or her own work but shows an incomplete understanding of evaluation criteria.
1 POINT	The student cannot identify or compare the use of geometric shapes in different works of art.	The student cannot identify geometric shapes.	The student's paper collage shows no understanding of geometric shapes.	The student makes no attempt to evaluate his or her own artwork.

Level 2 • Unit I • Lesson 6

	Art History and Culture	Aesthetic Perception	Creative Expression	Art Criticism
3 POINTS	The student can identify and compare the use of free-form shapes in different works of art.	The student accurately identifies free-form shapes in his or her environment.	The student's shadow puppet clearly illustrates a good use of free-form shapes.	The student thoughtfully and honestly evaluates his or her own work using the four steps of art criticism.
2 POINTS	The student's identification or comparison is weak or incomplete.	The student shows emerging awareness of free-form shapes but cannot consistently identify them.	The student's shadow puppet shows some awareness of free-form shapes.	The student attempts to evaluate his or her own work but shows an incomplete understanding of evaluation criteria.
1 POINT	The student cannot identify or compare the use of free-form shapes in different works of art.	The student cannot identify free-form shapes.	The student's shadow puppet shows no understanding of free-form shapes.	The student makes no attempt to evaluate his or her own artwork.

Creative Expression Rubrics

Level 2 • Unit 2 • Lesson 1

	Art History and Culture	Aesthetic Perception	Creative Expression	Art Criticism
3 POINTS	The student can identify and compare how Moroles and Smith selected used materials to create geometric forms.	The student accurately identifies geometric forms in his or her environment.	The student's sculpture clearly illustrates a good use of geometric forms.	The student thoughtfully and honestly evaluates his or her own work using the four steps of art criticism.
2 POINTS	The student's identification or comparison is weak or incomplete.	The student shows emerging awareness of geometric forms, but cannot consistently identify them.	The student's sculpture shows some geometric forms.	The student attempts to evaluate his or her own work but shows an incomplete understanding of evaluation criteria.
1 POINT	The student cannot identify or compare the use of materials used to create geometric forms in different works of art.	The student cannot identify geometric forms.	The student's sculpture shows no geometric forms.	The student does not attempt to evaluate his or her own artwork.

Level 2 • Unit 2 • Lesson 2

	Art History and Culture	Aesthetic Perception	Creative Expression	Art Criticism
3 POINTS	The student can identify the role of kings in ancient cultures and compare how kings are depicted in two works of art.	The student accurately identifies free-form forms in his or her environment.	The student's dream tree clearly illustrates a good use of types of lines.	The student thoughtfully and honestly evaluates his or her own work using the four steps of art criticism.
2 POINTS	The student's identification or comparison is weak or incomplete.	The student shows emerging awareness of free-form forms but cannot consistently identify them.	The student's relief clearly illustrates a good use of free-form forms.	The student attempts to evaluate his or her own work but shows an incomplete understanding of evaluation criteria.
1 POINT	The student cannot identify the role of kings or compare the depiction of kings in different works of art.	The student cannot identify free-form forms.	The student's relief shows some awareness of free-form forms.	The student does not attempt to evaluate his or her own artwork.

Creative Expression Rubrics

Level 2 • Unit 2 • Lesson 3

	Art History and Culture	Aesthetic Perception	Creative Expression	Art Criticism
3 POINTS	The student can identify the role of clowns and hunters in Pueblo and Inuit cultures and compare how they are depicted in two works of art.	The student accurately identifies body forms in his or her environment.	The student's sculpture clearly illustrates a good use of body forms.	The student thoughtfully and honestly evaluates his or her own work using the four steps of art criticism.
2 POINTS	The student's identification or comparison is weak or incomplete.	The student shows emerging awareness of body forms but cannot consistently identify them.	The student's sculpture shows some awareness of body forms.	The student attempts to evaluate his or her own work but shows an incomplete understanding of evaluation criteria.
1 POINT	The student cannot identify the role of clowns or hunters in Pueblo and Inuit culture or compare their depiction in different works of art.	The student cannot identify body forms.	The student's sculpture shows no understanding of body forms.	The student does not attempt to evaluate his or her own artwork.

Level 2 • Unit 2 • Lesson 4

	Art History and Culture	Aesthetic Perception	Creative Expression	Art Criticism
3 POINTS	The student can identify and compare the use of animal forms in a work of art.	The student accurately identifies animal forms in his or her environment.	The student's sculpture clearly illustrates a good use of animal forms.	The student thoughtfully and honestly evaluates his or her own work using the four steps of art criticism.
2 POINTS	The student's identification or comparison is weak or incomplete.	The student shows emerging awareness of animal forms but cannot consistently identify them.	The student's sculpture shows some awareness of animal forms.	The student attempts to evaluate his or her own work but shows an incomplete understanding of evaluation criteria.
1 POINT	The student cannot identify or compare the use of animal forms in different works of art.	The student cannot identify animal forms.	The student's sculpture shows no understanding of animal forms.	The student makes no attempt to evaluate his or her own artwork.

Creative Expression Rubrics

Level 2 • Unit 2 • Lesson 5

	Art History and Culture	Aesthetic Perception	Creative Expression	Art Criticism
3 POINTS	The student can compare how families are depicted in two works of art.	The student accurately identifies overlapping body shapes in students' environments.	The student's collage clearly illustrates a good use of people and space.	The student thoughtfully and honestly evaluates his or her own work using the four steps of art criticism.
2 POINTS	The student's comparison is weak or incomplete.	The student shows emerging awareness of people and space, but cannot consistently identify them.	The student's collage shows some awareness of people and space.	The student attempts to evaluate his or her own work but shows an incomplete understanding of evaluation criteria.
1 POINT	The student cannot compare how families are depicted in different works of art.	The student cannot identify overlapping body shapes.	The student's collage shows no understanding of people and space.	The student does not attempt to evaluate his or her own artwork.

Level 2 • Unit 2 • Lesson 6

	Art History and Culture	Aesthetic Perception	Creative Expression	Art Criticism
3 POINTS	The student can identify and compare the use of fruit in the works of art.	The student accurately identifies objects and space in the environment.	The student's still life clearly illustrates a good use of objects and space.	The student thoughtfully and honestly evaluates his or her own work using the four steps of art criticism.
2 POINTS	The student's identification or comparison is weak or incomplete.	The student shows emerging awareness of objects and space but cannot consistently identify them.	The student's still life shows some awareness of objects and space.	The student attempts to evaluate his or her own work but shows an incomplete understanding of evaluation criteria.
1 POINT	The student cannot identify or compare the use of fruit in different works of art.	The student cannot identify objects and space.	The student's still life shows no understanding of objects and space.	The student does not attempt to evaluate his or her own artwork.

Creative Expression Rubrics

Level 2 • Unit 3 • Lesson 1

	Art History and Culture	Aesthetic Perception	Creative Expression	Art Criticism
3 POINTS	The student can identify and compare two modern art paintings.	The student accurately identifies color and hue in his or her environment.	The student's painting clearly illustrates a good use of color and hue.	The student thoughtfully and honestly evaluates his or her own work using the four steps of art criticism.
2 POINTS	The student's identification or comparison is weak or incomplete.	The student shows emerging awareness of color and hue but cannot consistently identify them.	The student's painting shows some awareness of color and hue.	The student attempts to evaluate his or her own work but shows an incomplete understanding of evaluation criteria.
1 POINT	The students cannot identify or compare two modern art paintings.	The student cannot identify color and hue.	The student's painting shows no understanding of color and hue.	The student makes no attempt to evaluate his or her own artwork.

Level 2 • Unit 3 • Lesson 2

	Art History and Culture	Aesthetic Perception	Creative Expression	Art Criticism
3 POINTS	The student can identify and compare the use of warm hues in a work of art.	The student accurately identifies warm hues in his or her environment.	The student's resist clearly illustrates a good use of warm hues.	The student thoughtfully and honestly evaluates his or her own work using the four steps of art criticism.
2 POINTS	The student's identification or comparison is weak or incomplete.	The student shows emerging awareness of warm hues, but cannot consistently identify them.	The student's resist shows some awareness of warm hues.	The student attempts to evaluate his or her own work but shows an incomplete understanding of evaluation criteria.
1 POINT	The student cannot identify or compare the use of warm hues in different works of art.	The student cannot identify warm hues.	The student's resist shows no understanding of warm hues.	The student makes no attempt to evaluate his or her own artwork.

Creative Expression Rubrics

Level 2 • Unit 3 • Lesson 3

	Art History and Culture	Aesthetic Perception	Creative Expression	Art Criticism
3 POINTS	The student can identify that setting was important to Thomson and Kensett.	The student accurately identifies cool hues in his or her environment.	The student's landscape clearly illustrates a good use of cool hues.	The student thoughtfully and honestly evaluates his or her own work using the four steps of art criticism.
2 POINTS	The student's identification or comparison is weak or incomplete.	The student shows emerging awareness of cool hues, but cannot consistently identify them.	The student's landscape shows some awareness of cool hues.	The student attempts to evaluate his or her own work but shows an incomplete understanding of evaluation criteria.
1 POINT	The students cannot identify that setting was important to Thomson and Kensett.	The student cannot identify cool hues.	The student's landscape shows no understanding of cool hues.	The student makes no attempt to evaluate his or her own artwork.

Level 2 • Unit 3 • Lesson 4

	Art History and Culture	Aesthetic Perception	Creative Expression	Art Criticism
3 POINTS	The student can identify and compare the use of objects and contextual clues in two works of art.	The student accurately identifies value in his or her environment.	The student's painting clearly illustrates a good use of value.	The student thoughtfully and honestly evaluates his or her own work using the four steps of art criticism.
2 POINTS	The student's identification or comparison is weak or incomplete.	The student shows emerging awareness of value but cannot consistently identify them.	The student's painting shows some awareness of value.	The student attempts to evaluate his or her own work but shows an incomplete understanding of evaluation criteria.
1 POINT	The students cannot identify or compare the use of objects and contextual clues in different works of art.	The student cannot identify value.	The student's painting shows no understanding of value.	The student makes no attempt to evaluate his or her own artwork.

Creative Expression Rubrics

Level 2 • Unit 3 • Lesson 5

	Art History and Culture	Aesthetic Perception	Creative Expression	Art Criticism
3 POINTS	The student can identify and compare the use of light values in a work of art.	The student accurately identifies light values in his or her environment.	The student's painting clearly illustrates a good use of light values.	The student thoughtfully and honestly evaluates his or her own work using the four steps of art criticism.
2 POINTS	The student's identification or comparison is weak or incomplete.	The student shows emerging awareness of light values but cannot consistently identify them.	The student's painting shows some awareness of light values.	The student attempts to evaluate his or her own work but shows an incomplete understanding of evaluation criteria.
1 POINT	The student cannot identify or compare the use of light values in different works of art.	The student cannot identify light values.	The student's painting shows no understanding of light values.	The student makes no attempt to evaluate his or her own artwork.

Level 2 • Unit 3 • Lesson 6

	Art History and Culture	Aesthetic Perception	Creative Expression	Art Criticism
3 POINTS	The student can identify and compare the use of dark values to express feelings in works of art.	The student accurately identifies dark values in his or her environment.	The student's painting clearly illustrates a good use of dark values.	The student thoughtfully and honestly evaluates his or her own work using the four steps of art criticism.
2 POINTS	The student's identification or comparison is weak or incomplete.	The student shows emerging awareness of dark values but cannot consistently identify them.	The student's painting shows some awareness of dark values.	The student attempts to evaluate his or her own work but shows an incomplete understanding of evaluation criteria.
1 POINT	The students cannot identify or compare the use of dark values to express feelings in different works of art.	The student cannot identify dark values.	The student's painting shows no understanding of dark values.	The student makes no attempt to evaluate his or her own artwork.

Creative Expression Rubrics

Level 2 • Unit 4 • Lesson 1

	Art History and Culture	Aesthetic Perception	Creative Expression	Art Criticism
3 POINTS	The student can identify and compare the use of pattern and infer information about the cultures based on the works of art.	The student accurately identifies pattern and motif in his or her environment.	The student's print clearly illustrates a good use of pattern and motif.	The student thoughtfully and honestly evaluates his or her own work using the four steps of art criticism.
2 POINTS	The student's identification or comparison of pattern and motif is weak or incomplete.	The student shows emerging awareness of pattern and motif but cannot consistently identify them.	The student's print shows some awareness of pattern and motif.	The student attempts to evaluate his or her own work but shows an incomplete understanding of evaluation criteria.
1 POINT	The students cannot identify or compare the use of pattern and infer information about the cultures based on the works of art.	The student cannot identify pattern and motif.	The student's print shows no understanding of pattern and motif.	The student makes no attempt to evaluate his or her own artwork.

Level 2 • Unit 4 • Lesson 2

	Art History and Culture	Aesthetic Perception	Creative Expression	Art Criticism
3 POINTS	The student can identify and compare the use of patterns in nature in a work of art.	The student accurately identifies patterns in nature in his or her environment.	The student's natural object clearly illustrates a good use of patterns in nature.	The student thoughtfully and honestly evaluates his or her own work using the four steps of art criticism.
2 POINTS	The student's identification or comparison of patterns in nature is weak or incomplete.	The student shows emerging awareness of patterns in nature but cannot consistently identify them.	The student's natural object shows some awareness of patterns in nature.	The student attempts to evaluate his or her own work but shows an incomplete understanding of evaluation criteria.
1 POINT	The student cannot identify or compare the use of patterns in nature in different works of art.	The student cannot identify patterns in nature.	The student's natural object shows no understanding of patterns in nature.	The student makes no attempt to evaluate his or her own artwork.

Creative Expression Rubrics

Level 2 • Unit 4 • Lesson 3

	Art History and Culture	Aesthetic Perception	Creative Expression	Art Criticism
3 POINTS	The student can identify and compare the use of rhythm in a work of art.	The student accurately identifies rhythm in his or her environment.	The student's still life clearly illustrates a good use of rhythm.	The student thoughtfully and honestly evaluates his or her own work using the four steps of art criticism.
2 POINTS	The student's identification or comparison of the use of rhythm is weak or incomplete.	The student shows emerging awareness of rhythm but cannot consistently identify them.	The student's still life shows some awareness of rhythm.	The student attempts to evaluate his or her own work but shows an incomplete understanding of evaluation criteria.
1 POINT	The student cannot identify or compare the use of rhythm in different works of art.	The student cannot identify rhythm.	The student's still life shows no understanding of rhythm.	The student makes no attempt to evaluate his or her own artwork.

Level 2 • Unit 4 • Lesson 4

	Art History and Culture	Aesthetic Perception	Creative Expression	Art Criticism
3 POINTS	The student can identify and compare the inspiration for two works of art.	The student accurately identifies rhythm and form in his or her environment.	The student's storyteller doll clearly illustrates a good use of rhythm and form.	The student thoughtfully and honestly evaluates his or her own work using the four steps of art criticism.
2 POINTS	The student's identification or comparison is weak or incomplete.	The student shows emerging awareness of rhythm and form, but cannot consistently identify them.	The student's storyteller doll shows some awareness of rhythm and form.	The student attempts to evaluate his or her own work but shows an incomplete understanding of evaluation criteria.
1 POINT	The students cannot identify or compare the inspiration in different works of art.	The student cannot identify rhythm and form.	The student's storyteller doll shows no understanding of rhythm and form.	The student makes no attempt to evaluate his or her own artwork.

Creative Expression Rubrics

Level 2 • Unit 4 • Lesson 5

	Art History and Culture	Aesthetic Perception	Creative Expression	Art Criticism
3 POINTS	The student can identify and compare the way artists depict dancing in art.	The student accurately identifies diagonal movement in his or her environment.	The student's computer drawing clearly illustrates a good use of diagonal movement.	The student thoughtfully and honestly evaluates his or her own work using the four steps of art criticism.
2 POINTS	The student's identification or comparison of the use of diagonal movement is weak or incomplete.	The student shows emerging awareness of diagonal movement, but cannot consistently identify it.	The student's computer drawing shows some awareness of diagonal movement.	The student attempts to evaluate his or her own work but shows an incomplete understanding of evaluation criteria.
1 POINT	The students cannot identify or compare the way artists depict dancing.	The student cannot identify diagonal movement.	The student's computer drawing shows no understanding of diagonal movement.	The student makes no attempt to evaluate his or her own artwork.

Level 2 • Unit 4 • Lesson 6

	Art History and Culture	Aesthetic Perception	Creative Expression	Art Criticism
3 POINTS	The student can identify and compare the use of curving movement in a work of art.	The student accurately identifies curving movement in his or her environment.	The student's painting clearly illustrates a good use of curving movement.	The student thoughtfully and honestly evaluates his or her own work using the four steps of art criticism.
2 POINTS	The student's identification or comparison of curving movement is weak or incomplete.	The student shows emerging awareness of curving movement but cannot consistently identify it.	The student's painting shows some awareness of curving movement.	The student attempts to evaluate his or her own work but shows an incomplete understanding of evaluation criteria.
1 POINT	The student cannot identify or compare the use of curving movement in different works of art.	The student cannot identify curving movement.	The student's painting shows no understanding of curving movement.	The student makes no attempt to evaluate his or her own artwork.

Creative Expression Rubrics

Level 2 • Unit 5 • Lesson 1

	Art History and Culture	Aesthetic Perception	Creative Expression	Art Criticism
3 POINTS	The student can identify and compare the use of jars in ancient cultures.	The student accurately identifies balance and symmetry in containers.	The student's paper jar clearly illustrates a good use of balance and symmetry.	The student thoughtfully and honestly evaluates his or her own work using the four steps of art criticism.
2 POINTS	The student's identification or comparison is weak or incomplete.	The student shows emerging awareness of balance and symmetry, but cannot consistently identify them.	The student's paper jar shows some awareness of balance and symmetry.	The student attempts to evaluate his or her own work but shows an incomplete understanding of evaluation criteria.
1 POINT	The students cannot identify or compare the use of jars in ancient cultures.	The student cannot identify balance and symmetry.	The student's paper jar shows no understanding of balance and symmetry.	The student makes no attempt to evaluate his or her own artwork.

Level 2 • Unit 5 • Lesson 2

	Art History and Culture	Aesthetic Perception	Creative Expression	Art Criticism
3 POINTS	The student can identify and compare the use of heroes in a work of art.	The student accurately identifies balance in people in his or her environments.	The student's hero drawing clearly illustrates a good use of balance in people.	The student thoughtfully and honestly evaluates his or her own work using the four steps of art criticism.
2 POINTS	The student's identification or comparison is weak or incomplete.	The student shows emerging awareness of balance in people but cannot consistently identify it.	The student's hero drawing shows some awareness of balance in people.	The student attempts to evaluate his or her own work but shows an incomplete understanding of evaluation criteria.
1 POINT	The student cannot identify or compare the use of heroes in different works of art.	The student cannot identify balance in people.	The student's hero drawing shows no understanding of balance in people.	The student makes no attempt to evaluate his or her own artwork.

Creative Expression Rubrics

Level 2 • Unit 5 • Lesson 3

	Art History and Culture	Aesthetic Perception	Creative Expression	Art Criticism
3 POINTS	The student can identify that groups of people portrayed in a work of art often have a significant meaning to the artist.	The student accurately identifies emphasis in his or her environment.	The student's drawing clearly illustrates a good use of emphasis.	The student thoughtfully and honestly evaluates his or her own work using the four steps of art criticism.
2 POINTS	The student's identification or comparison is weak or incomplete.	The student shows emerging awareness of emphasis but cannot consistently identify it.	The student's drawing shows some awareness of emphasis.	The student attempts to evaluate his or her own work but shows an incomplete understanding of evaluation criteria.
1 POINT	The students cannot identify that groups of people portrayed in a work of art often have a significant meaning to the artist.	The student cannot identify emphasis.	The student's drawing shows no understanding of emphasis.	The student makes no attempt to evaluate his or her own artwork.

Level 2 • Unit 5 • Lesson 4

	Art History and Culture	Aesthetic Perception	Creative Expression	Art Criticism
3 POINTS	The student can identify that artists often paint buildings they are familiar with and that the buildings often have a purpose.	The student accurately identifies emphasis using contrast in his or her environment.	The student's night scene clearly illustrates a good use of emphasis using contrast.	The student thoughtfully and honestly evaluates his or her own work using the four steps of art criticism.
2 POINTS	The student's identification or comparison is weak or incomplete.	The student shows emerging awareness of emphasis using contrast but cannot consistently identify it.	The student's night scene shows some awareness of emphasis using contrast.	The student attempts to evaluate his or her own work but shows an incomplete understanding of evaluation criteria.
1 POINT	The students cannot identify that artists often paint buildings they are familiar with and that the buildings often have a purpose.	The student cannot identify emphasis using contrast.	The student's night scene shows no understanding of emphasis using contrast.	The student makes no attempt to evaluate his or her own artwork.

Creative Expression Rubrics

Level 2 • Unit 5 • Lesson 5

	Art History and Culture	Aesthetic Perception	Creative Expression	Art Criticism
3 POINTS	The student can identify and compare the use of tactile texture in a work of art.	The student accurately identifies tactile texture in his or her environment.	The student's stitchery clearly illustrates a good use of tactile texture.	The student thoughtfully and honestly evaluates his or her own work using the four steps of art criticism.
2 POINTS	The student's identification or comparison is weak or incomplete.	The student shows emerging awareness of tactile texture, but cannot consistently identify it.	The student's stitchery shows some awareness of tactile texture.	The student attempts to evaluate his or her own work but shows an incomplete understanding of evaluation criteria.
1 POINT	The student cannot identify or compare the use of tactile texture in different works of art.	The student cannot identify tactile texture.	The student's stitchery shows no understanding of tactile texture.	The student makes no attempt to evaluate his or her own artwork.

Level 2 • Unit 5 • Lesson 6

	Art History and Culture	Aesthetic Perception	Creative Expression	Art Criticism
3 POINTS	The student can recognize that artists portray portrait subjects in clothing that describes the subject.	The student accurately identifies visual texture in his or her environment.	The student's texture rubbing collage clearly illustrates a good use of visual texture.	The student thoughtfully and honestly evaluates his or her own work using the four steps of art criticism.
2 POINTS	The student's recognition is weak or incomplete.	The student shows emerging awareness of visual texture, but cannot consistently identify it.	The student's texture rubbing collage shows some awareness of visual texture.	The student attempts to evaluate his or her own work but shows an incomplete understanding of evaluation criteria.
1 POINT	The students cannot recognize that artists portray portrait subjects in clothing that describes the subject.	The student cannot identify visual texture.	The student's texture rubbing collage shows no understanding of visual texture.	The student makes no attempt to evaluate his or her own artwork.

Creative Expression Rubrics

Level 2 • Unit 6 • Lesson 1

	Art History and Culture	Aesthetic Perception	Creative Expression	Art Criticism
3 POINTS	The student can identify that different colors have special meanings in different cultures.	The student accurately identifies harmony of shape and form in his or her environment.	The student's tile clearly illustrates a good use of harmony of color.	The student thoughtfully and honestly evaluates his or her own work using the four steps of art criticism.
2 POINTS	The student's identification or comparison is weak or incomplete.	The student shows emerging awareness of harmony of color but cannot consistently identify them.	The student's tile shows some awareness of harmony of color.	The student attempts to evaluate his or her own work but shows an incomplete understanding of evaluation criteria.
1 POINT	The students cannot identify that different colors have special meanings in different cultures.	The student cannot identify harmony of color.	The student's tile shows no understanding of harmony of color.	The student makes no attempt to evaluate his or her own artwork.

Level 2 • Unit 6 • Lesson 2

	Art History and Culture	Aesthetic Perception	Creative Expression	Art Criticism
3 POINTS	The student can identify and compare the use of animals based on the artist's location.	The student accurately identifies harmony of shape and form in his or her environment.	The student's animal family clearly illustrates a good use of harmony of shape and form.	The student thoughtfully and honestly evaluates his or her own work using the four steps of art criticism.
2 POINTS	The student's identification or comparison is weak or incomplete.	The student shows emerging awareness of harmony of shape and form but cannot consistently identify it.	The student's animal family shows some awareness of harmony of shape and form.	The student attempts to evaluate his or her own work but shows an incomplete understanding of evaluation criteria.
1 POINT	The students cannot identify or compare the use of animals based on the artist's location.	The student cannot identify harmony of shape and form.	The student's animal family shows no understanding of harmony of shape and form.	The student makes no attempt to evaluate his or her own artwork.

Creative Expression Rubrics

Level 2 • Unit 6 • Lesson 3

	Art History and Culture	Aesthetic Perception	Creative Expression	Art Criticism
3 POINTS	The student can identify and compare the style of two works of art.	The student accurately identifies variety of color in everyday objects.	The student's underwater print clearly illustrates a good use of variety of color.	The student thoughtfully and honestly evaluates his or her own work using the four steps of art criticism.
2 POINTS	The student's identification or comparison is weak or incomplete.	The student shows emerging awareness of variety of color but cannot consistently identify it.	The student's underwater print shows some awareness of variety of color.	The student attempts to evaluate his or her own work but shows an incomplete understanding of evaluation criteria.
1 POINT	The students cannot identify or compare the style of two works of art.	The student cannot identify variety of color.	The student's underwater print shows no understanding of variety of color.	The student makes no attempt to evaluate his or her own artwork.

Level 2 • Unit 6 • Lesson 4

	Art History and Culture	Aesthetic Perception	Creative Expression	Art Criticism
3 POINTS	The student can identify and compare the style of two works of art.	The student accurately identifies variety of shape and form in everyday objects.	The student's fantasy bird clearly illustrates a good use of variety of shape and form.	The student thoughtfully and honestly evaluates his or her own work using the four steps of art criticism.
2 POINTS	The student's identification or comparison is weak or incomplete.	The student shows emerging awareness of variety of shape and form but cannot consistently identify it.	The student's fantasy bird shows some awareness of variety of shape and form.	The student attempts to evaluate his or her own work but shows an incomplete understanding of evaluation criteria.
1 POINT	The student cannot identify or compare the style of two works of art.	The student cannot identify variety of shape and form.	The student's fantasy bird shows no understanding of variety of shape and form.	The student makes no attempt to evaluate his or her own artwork.

Creative Expression Rubrics

Level 2 • Unit 6 • Lesson 5

	Art History and Culture	Aesthetic Perception	Creative Expression	Art Criticism
3 POINTS	The student can identify that some carousels feature animals other than horses.	The student accurately identifies unity in sculpture in the environment.	The student's stuffed paper animal clearly illustrates a good use of unity in sculpture.	The student thoughtfully and honestly evaluates his or her own work using the four steps of art criticism.
2 POINTS	The student's identification is weak or incomplete.	The student shows emerging awareness of unity in sculpture but cannot consistently identify it.	The student's stuffed paper animal shows some awareness of unity in sculpture.	The student attempts to evaluate his or her own work but shows an incomplete understanding of evaluation criteria.
1 POINT	The students cannot identify that some carousels feature animals other than horses.	The student cannot identify unity in sculpture.	The student's stuffed paper animal shows no understanding of unity in sculpture.	The student makes no attempt to evaluate his or her own artwork.

Level 2 • Unit 6 • Lesson 6

	Art History and Culture	Aesthetic Perception	Creative Expression	Art Criticism
3 POINTS	The student can identify and compare the use of unity in architecture in a work of art.	The student accurately identifies unity in architecture in the environment.	The student's texture cityscape clearly illustrates a good use of unity in architecture.	The student thoughtfully and honestly evaluates his or her own work using the four steps of art criticism.
2 POINTS	The student's identification or comparison is weak or incomplete.	The student shows emerging awareness of unity in architecture but cannot consistently identify it.	The student's texture cityscape shows some awareness of unity in architecture.	The student attempts to evaluate his or her own work but shows an incomplete understanding of evaluation criteria.
1 POINT	The student cannot identify or compare the use of unity in architecture in different works of art.	The student cannot identify unity in architecture.	The student's texture cityscape shows no understanding of unity in architecture.	The student makes no attempt to evaluate his or her own artwork.